A Montessori Workbook
Volume 1

3-6 years

Exercises to develop visual discrimination,
fine motor skills, numbers, phonics, and more.

Punum Bhatia, PhD

For my children,
who led me to Montessori and
have always been my inspiration.

MONTESSORI CASA
INTERNATIONAL

144 Rampart Way, Denver, CO 80230

Printed in the USA
ISBN: 978-0-9975938-0-8
All rights reserved

Author Punum Bhatia, PhD
Cover photo by Kelley Priddy. Images designed by Freepik.com.
Images designed by Vecteezy.com. Moon illustration designed by Tintins from www.flaticon.com.
Sydney Opera House designed by ArtFavor at All-free-download.com.
Lady bug designed by VectorPortal.com. Layout by Jennie Wren.

Table of Contents

Introduction

At the turn of the 20th century, Dr. Maria Montessori discovered a revolutionary way of directing young children's learning; in contrast to the teacher-centered approach prevalent at the time, she realized that children learned more effectively if adults provided them with a calm, ordered space of the Montessori 'prepared environment' that gave them a sense of equality and empowerment. She describes this environment as a place where the child was nurtured, for its design meets his needs for self-construction and helps him reveal his personality and growth patterns to us. In the calm, ordered space of the Montessori 'prepared environment', children work on activities of their own choosing and at their own pace. They experience a blend of freedom and self-discipline in a place specially designed to meet their developmental needs.

A collection of materials (apparatus) is displayed on the shelves, with everything carefully ordered and in its place. The materials entice the child because they are placed in the center of his vision, are within easy reach, and because they have a sensory appeal, varying in color, shape, size, texture, and possibilities of manipulation. The array of sensory contrasts, however, suggests purposeful variation rather than a random placement of brightly colored objects. The apparatus helps children learn basic concepts and relationships at different levels of abstraction by ensuring that the activities are based on physical manipulation of objects and progress through imagery to symbolic representation. The adults in the classroom unobtrusively demonstrate the use of the materials and then leave the child to work with them, intervening as needed.

The activities provided in this book are meant to supplement the child's learning in a Montessori classroom. A bit of advice:

- Try to work closely with your child as s/he goes through this workbook. S/he needs your guidance and help. It is best to sit on his/her non-dominant side when working together.

- In the activities where you must trace the letters or numbers, make your movements slow and graceful. Repeat as many times as you think necessary.

- There is no sequence to this workbook. Allow your child to move freely within it – cutting, writing, coloring, etc.

- Never force your child to work on the book or set a minimum or maximum time limit.

- There should be no rewards or punishments. If your child was not able to do an activity, it simply means that it was not the right time or that your child was not ready for that step. Try again at a later time.

- It is most important that you both have fun and that this workbook provides him/her pleasure as s/he recognizes materials he has worked with at school – sort of like meeting an old friend!

Development of
of
Visual Discrimination

Maria Montessori recognized that nature had endowed the young child with heightened sensory awareness to assist him/her in concept formation. In Montessori classrooms, the teachers realize that the sensitive period for sensory exploration and refinement must not be wasted. The child learns to distinguish volume, size, colors, and geometric shapes with concrete materials. S/he has the opportunity to repeat and refine his/her sensory perceptions. Gradually as his/her powers of perception have been sharpened s/he will be able to detect increasingly fine differences in stimuli.

The first part of this workbook is dedicated to these activities that the child does concretely in school. To begin, show your child how to follow the outline of the shapes with the index and middle finger together in a counter clockwise direction. As you do so, name the shape and then invite your child to have a turn.

The Square

Trace the square in the direction of the arrow.

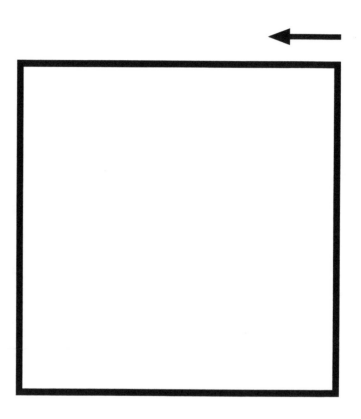

Color the squares below:

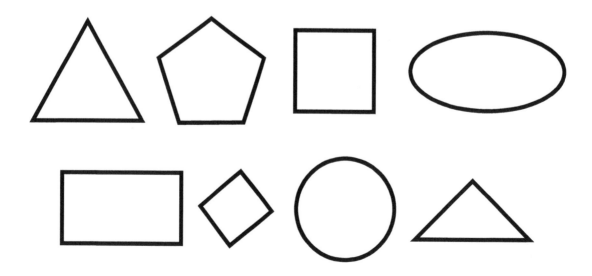

The Circle

Trace the circle in the direction of the arrow.

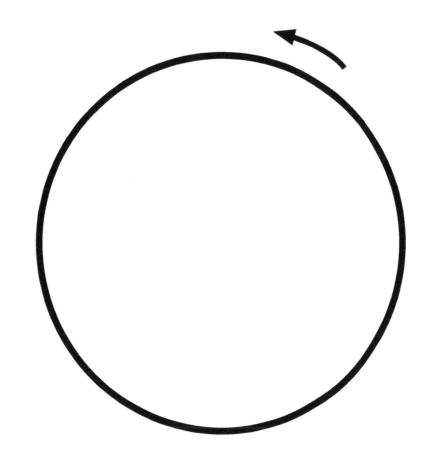

Color the circles below:

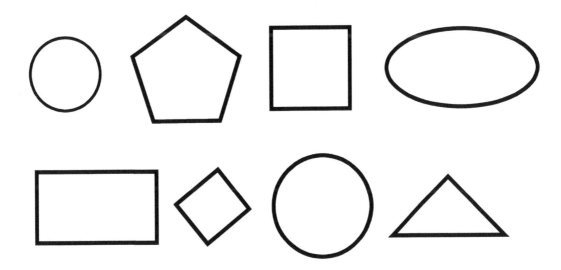

The Triangle

Trace the triangle in the direction of the arrow.

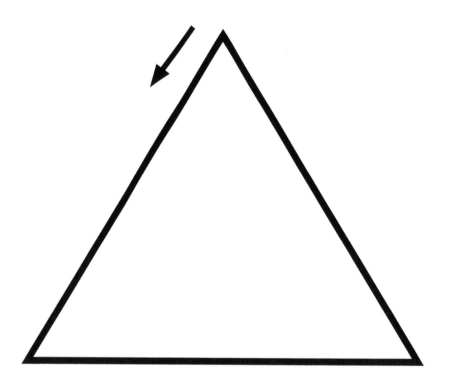

Color the triangles below:

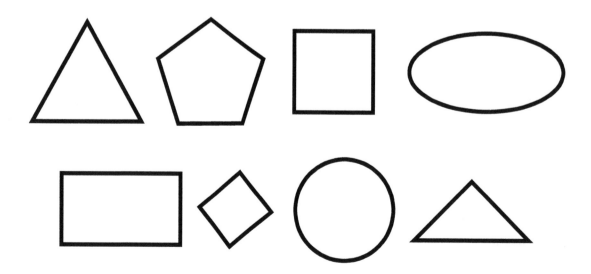

The Pink Tower

Color the squares pink.

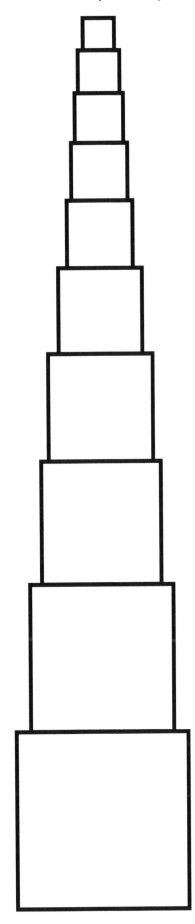

The Pink Tower

Color the biggest square pink.

The Pink Tower

Color the smallest square pink.

Color Box 1
Color the tablets red, blue and yellow.

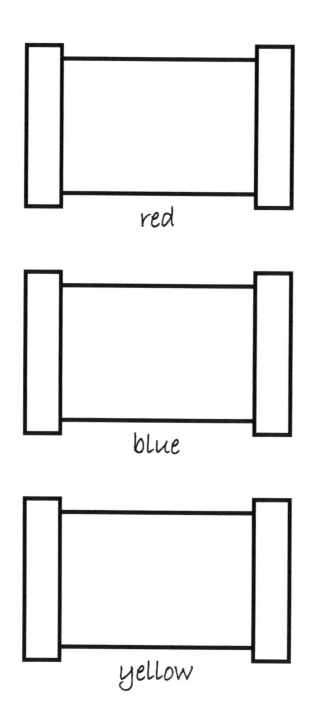

red

blue

yellow

Color the rubber duck yellow.

Color the apple red.

Color the hat blue.

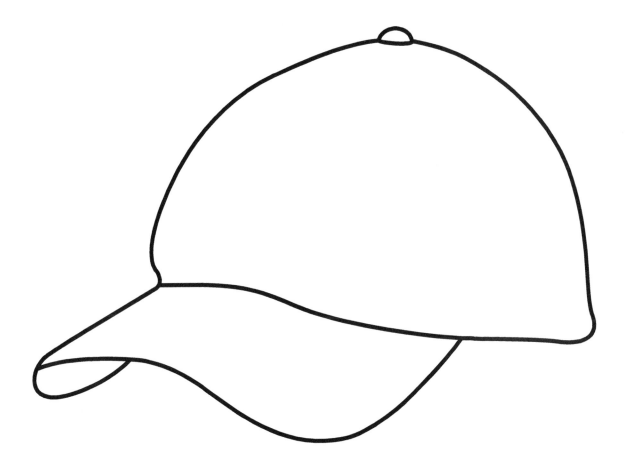

Brown Stair

Color the rectangles brown.

Brown Stair

Color the broadest rectangle brown.

Brown Stair

Color the narrowest rectangle brown.

Pink Tower and Brown Stair

Color the squares pink and rectangles brown.

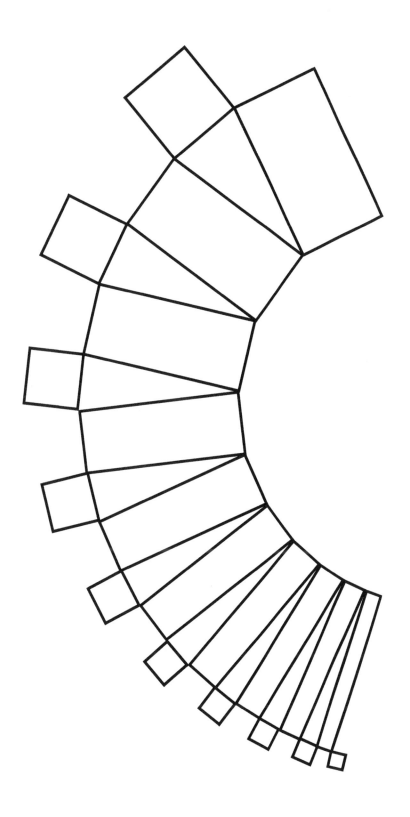

Pink Tower and Brown Stair

Color the squares pink and rectangles brown.

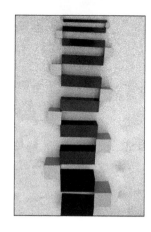

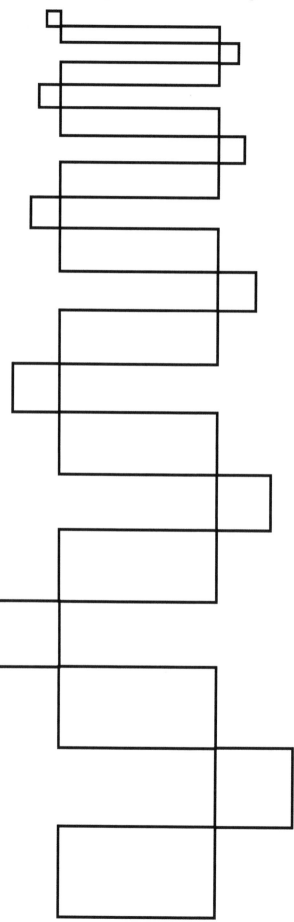

Pink Tower and Brown Stair

Color the squares pink and rectangles brown.

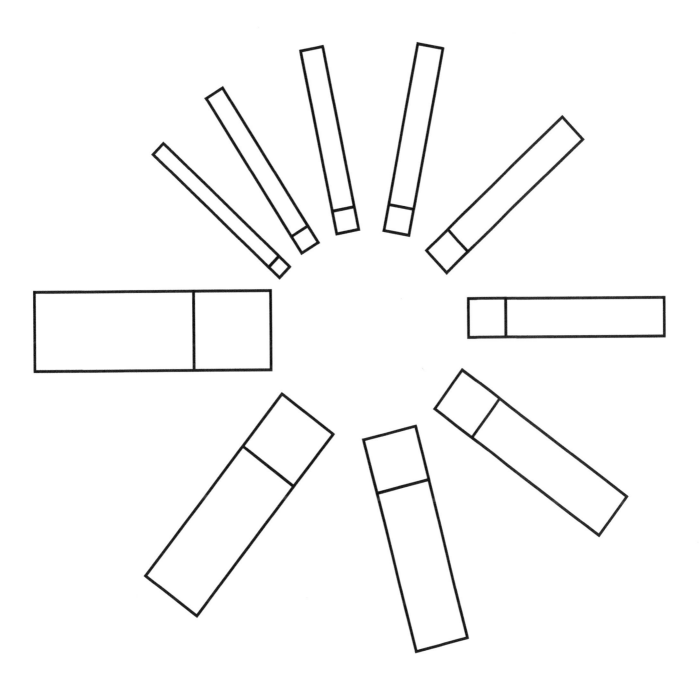

Letters
and
Sounds

While it is generally accepted that we are born with an innate capacity for acquiring language, it is also realized that babies and children's language development is linked to the quality of support they receive from adults. Montessori identified a sensitive period for language during the first six years of a child's life. This makes it an optimum time for acquiring languages and becoming competent language users. Toward the time they turn three years of age, the child manifests a particular interest in sounds and letters.

At school s/he will be introduced to sandpaper letters, which will introduce him/her to the sounds of the letters. This workbook compliments that process. Carefully follow the shape of the letter with the index and middle finger, indicating at the same time the sound of the letter clearly. Invite him/her to trace the letter and say the sound. When you introduce the objects to be colored emphasize the initial sound.

The other exercises in this section help prepare the hand for writing.

Connect the dotted lines:

Connect the dotted lines:

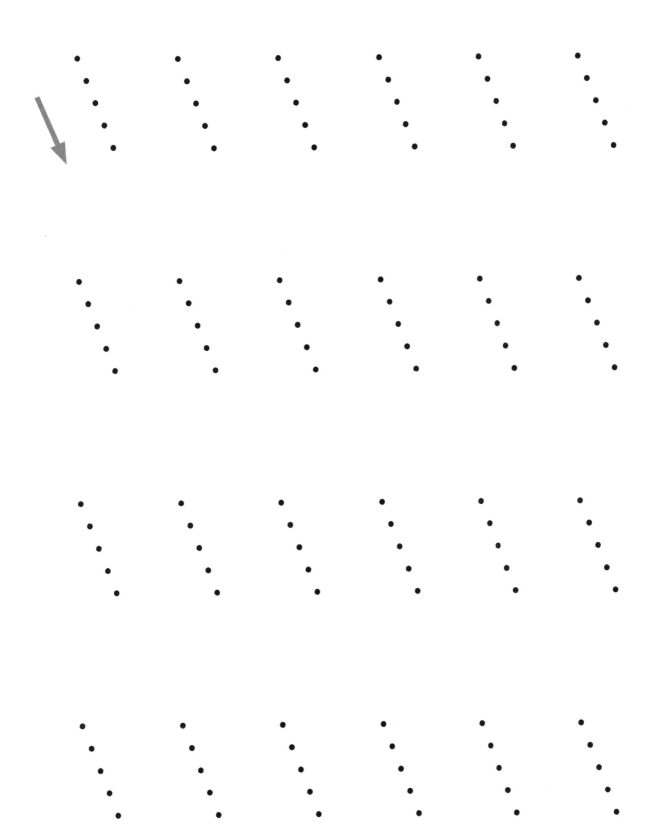

Connect the dotted lines:

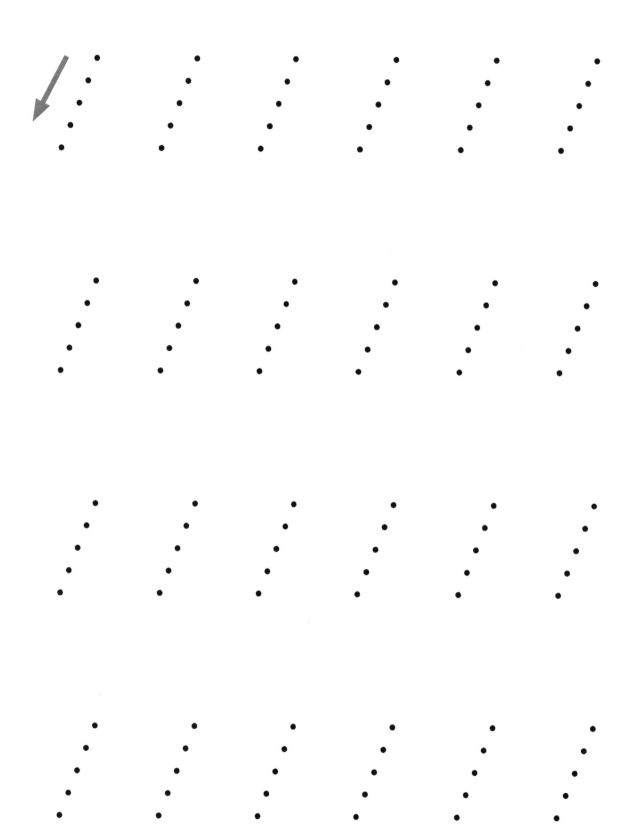

Connect the dotted lines:

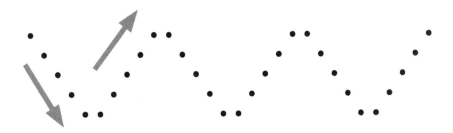

29

Copy each shape in the space provided.

│	
─	
○	
+	
/	

Metal Insets

Fill in the outline of the metal insets like the sample.

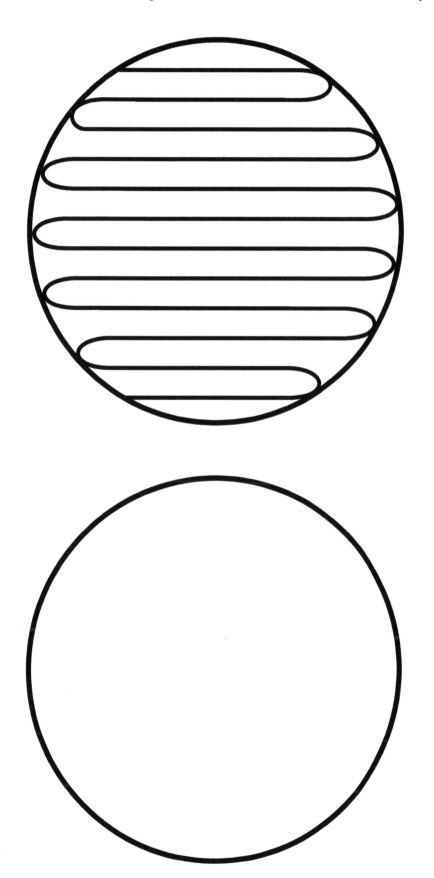

Metal Insets

Fill in the outline of the metal insets like the sample.

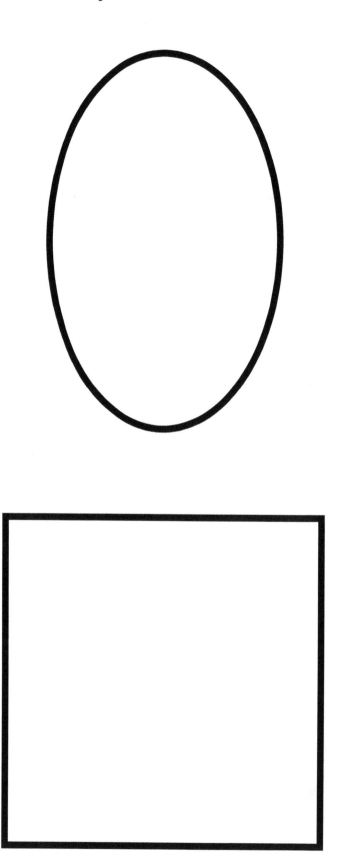

Metal Insets

Fill in the outline of the metal insets like the sample.

Follow the outline of the letter with two fingers.

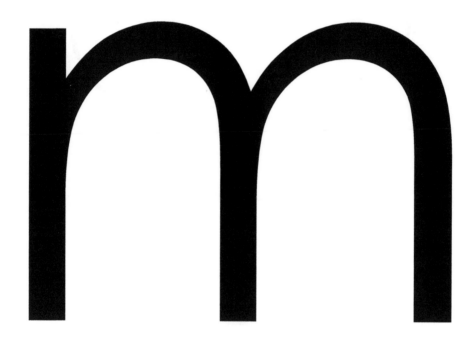

Color the **m**oon, **m**ouse and **m**onkey.

Follow the outline of the letter with two fingers.

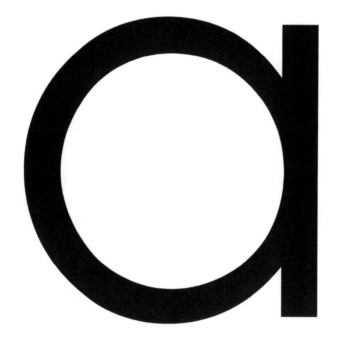

Color the **a**irplane, **a**lligator and **a**pple.

Follow the outline of the letter with two fingers.

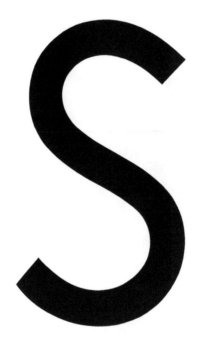

Color the **s**andals, **s**tar and **s**unflower.

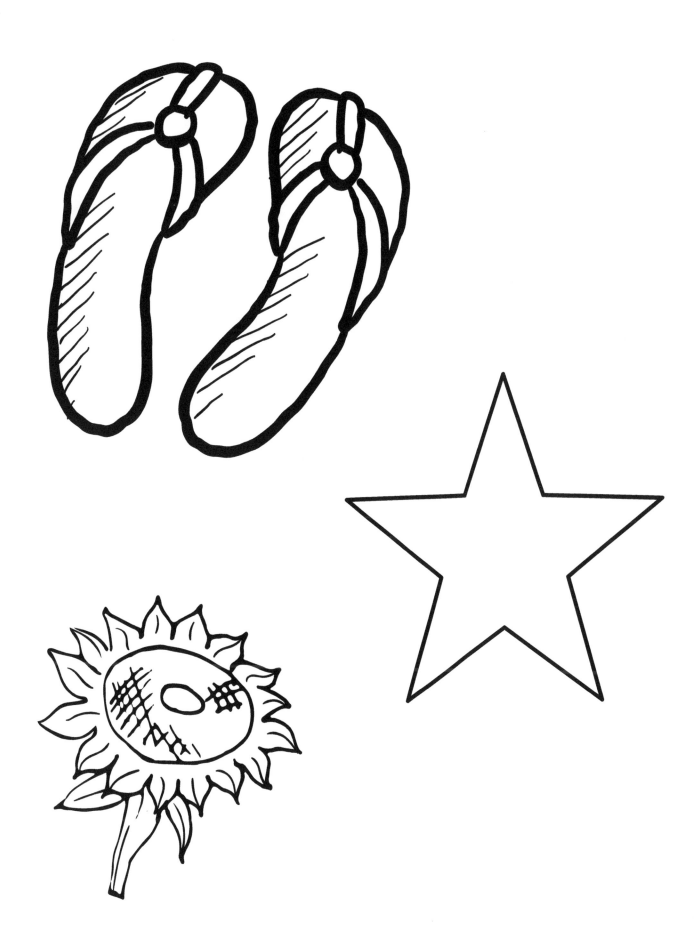

Follow the outline of the letter with two fingers.

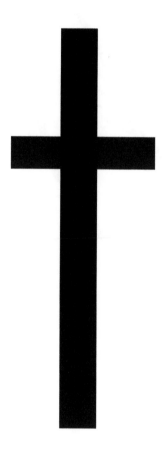

Color the **t**ree, **t**urtle and **t**rain.

Follow the outline of the letter with two fingers.

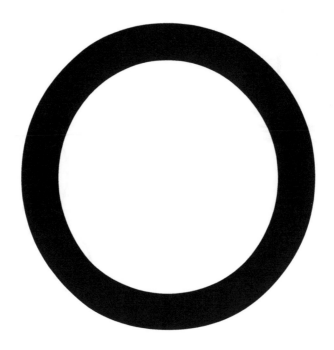

Color the **o**range, **o**wl and **o**ctopus.

Follow the outline of the letter with two fingers.

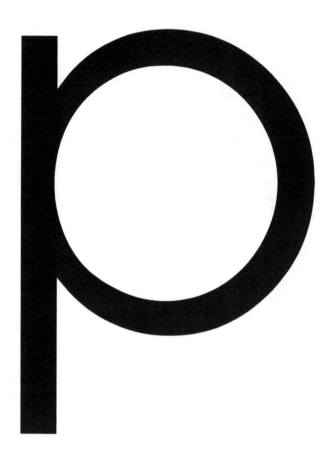

Color the **p**enguin, **p**umpkin and **p**ig.

Follow the outline of the letter with two fingers.

Color the **i**gloo, **i**nchworm and **i**nsect.

Follow the outline of the letter with two fingers.

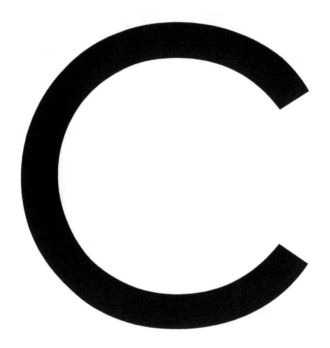

Color the **c**at, **c**arrot and **c**ake.

Cut the pictures below and match them to the initial sound.
Stick them in the right box.

m   a   s   t

Cut the pictures below and match them to the initial sound.
Stick them in the right box.

o   p   i   c

Answers: o - orange, p - pumpkin, i - igloo, and c - cake.

PRINT PRACTICE

m

a

s

t

PRINT PRACTICE

o

p

i

c

PRINT PRACTICE

Follow the outline of the letter with two fingers.

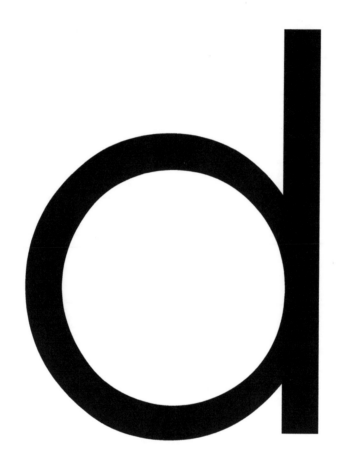

Color the **d**og, **d**rum and **d**inosaur.

Follow the outline of the letter with two fingers.

Color the **u**mbrella, **u**ncle Sam and **u**nderwear.

Follow the outline of the letter with two fingers.

Color the **r**ainbow, **r**abbit and **r**ocket.

Follow the outline of the letter with two fingers.

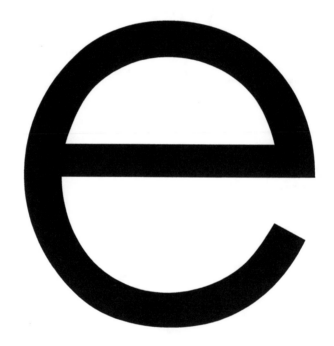

Color the **e**lephant, **e**gg and **e**ngine.

65

Follow the outline of the letter with two fingers.

Color the lion, lamp and ladybug.

Follow the outline of the letter with two fingers.

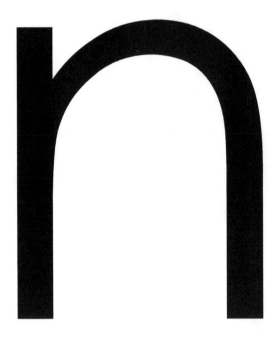

Color the **n**est, **n**uts and **n**urse.

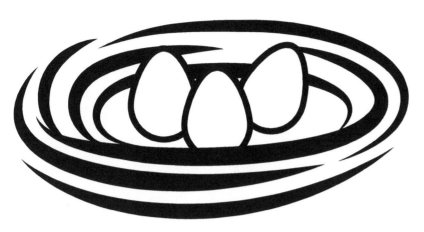

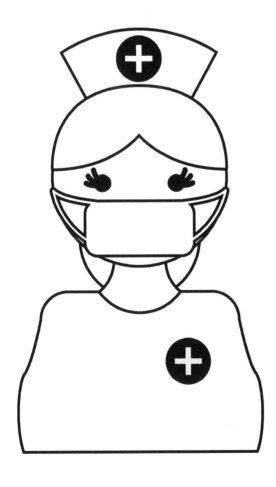

Follow the outline of the letter with two fingers.

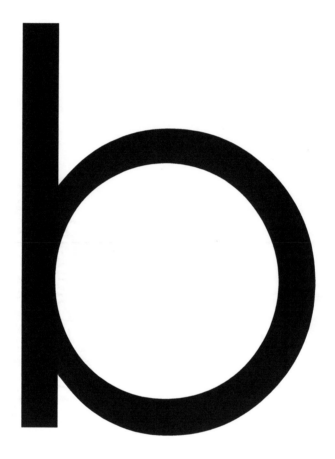

Color the **b**ear, **b**ee and **b**all.

Follow the outline of the letter with two fingers.

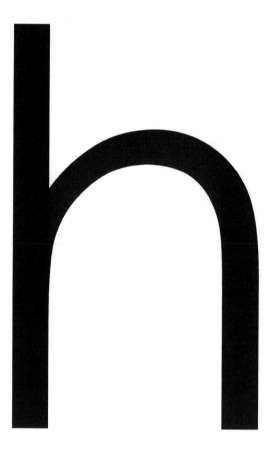

Color the **h**elicopter, **h**orse and **h**ammer.

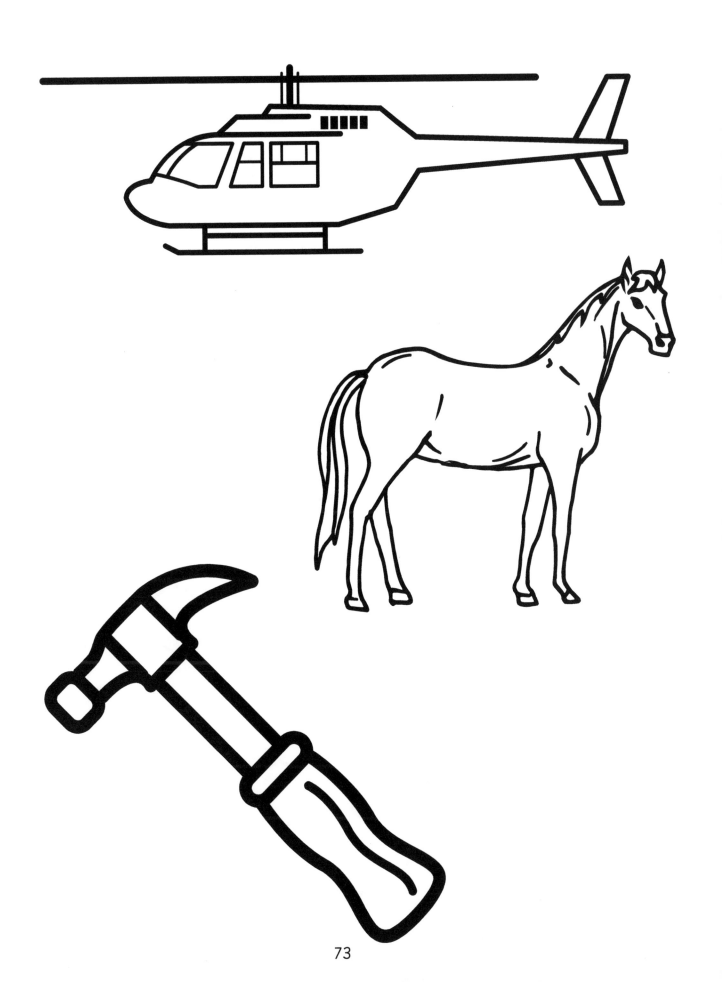

Cut the pictures below and match them to the initial sound.
Stick them in the right box.

d u r e

Cut the pictures below and match them to the initial sound.
Stick them in the right box.

l   n   b   h

Answers: l - ladybug, n - nest, b - ball, and h - hammer.

PRINT PRACTICE

d

u

r

e

PRINT PRACTICE

l

n

b

h

PRINT PRACTICE

WORD BUILDING

Advice to parents: when your child shows an inclination, ask him/her to identify the picture and then ask, "What is the first sound you hear in _____?" Have him/her write the letter in the first box. Then ask, "What is the next sound you hear in _____?" and so on.

Read the sentence below and draw a picture in the box.

The cat sat on the mat.

The man has a big dog.

Read the sentence below and draw a picture in the box.

The red mug is hot.

The fox is in the tub.

Numbers

Dr. Montessori recognized that children are born with a particular kind of mind, one that is naturally inclined towards order. She called this 'the mathematical mind' – a term borrowed from the French physicist and philosopher Blaise Pascal. She knew that children aged six and under learned best through their senses and hands - on manipulation. So she concluded that mathematical concepts must be introduced to the children in a concrete form before their abstract representation.

Children love to count and it is easy to get involved and count with them. Play together and count the red cars they see as you drive to the grocery store or the chocolate cup cakes in the pastry shop! Look for numbers all around you – on buildings or license plates – and read them with your child. In this section, the workbook compliments what they have been learning in school. Trace the numbers with your index and middle finger saying the number at the same time. Invite your child to repeat the exercise. The subsequent exercises will help them practice their number skills.

Follow the outline of the number with two fingers.

Color 1 apple.

Follow the outline of the number with two fingers.

Color **2** bees on the honeycomb.

Follow the outline of the number with two fingers.

Color **3** birds.

Follow the outline of the number with two fingers.

Color **4** drums.

Follow the outline of the number with two fingers.

Color **5** books.

Follow the outline of the number with two fingers.

Color **6** flowers.

Follow the outline of the number with two fingers.

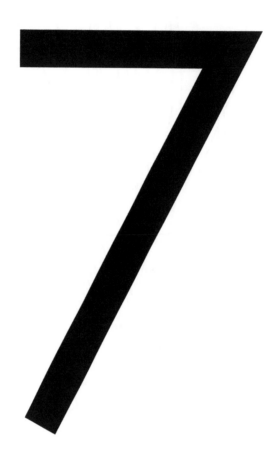

Color **7** fish in the bowl.

Follow the outline of the number with two fingers.

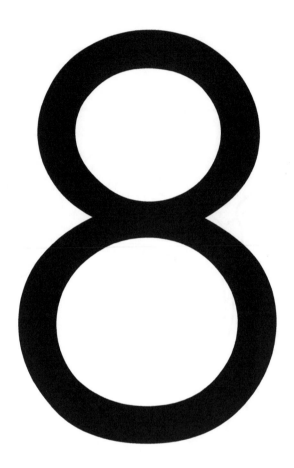

Color **8** donuts on the cart.

Follow the outline of the number with two fingers.

Color **9** paint streaks in different colors.

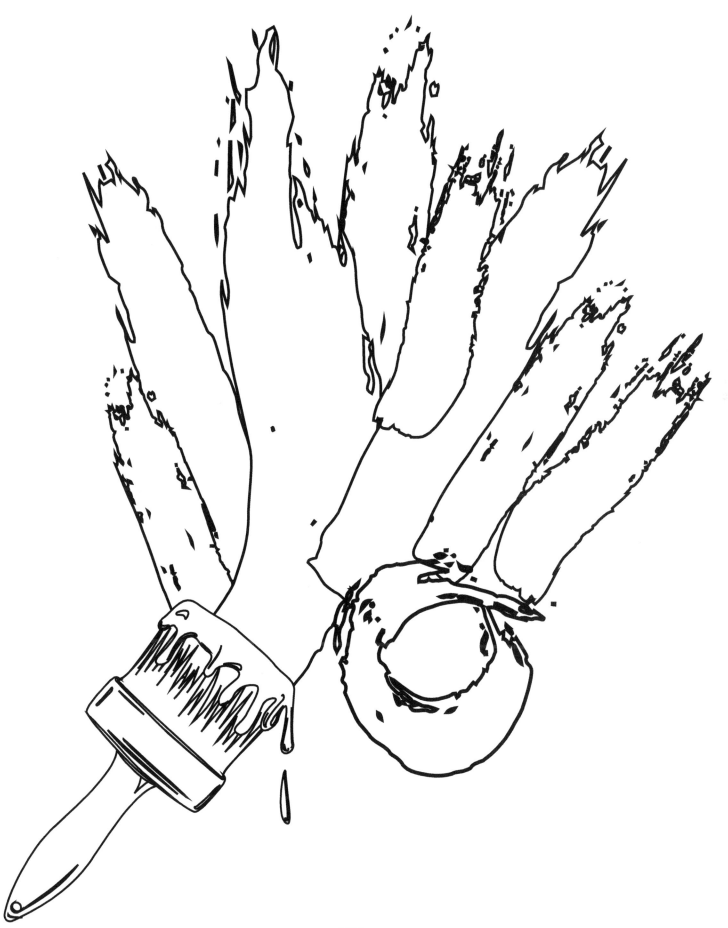

Follow the outline of the number with two fingers.

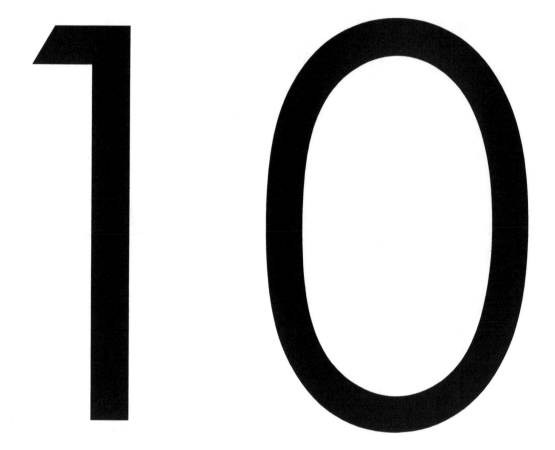

Color **10** balloons.

NUMBER RODS AND CARDS

Count the rods and write the number next to it.

____

____

____

____

____

____

____

____

____

____

SHORT BEAD STAIR

Color the bead stair as follows:

1 Red
2 Green
3 Pink
4 Yellow
5 Light Blue
6 Purple
7 White
8 Brown
9 Royal Blue

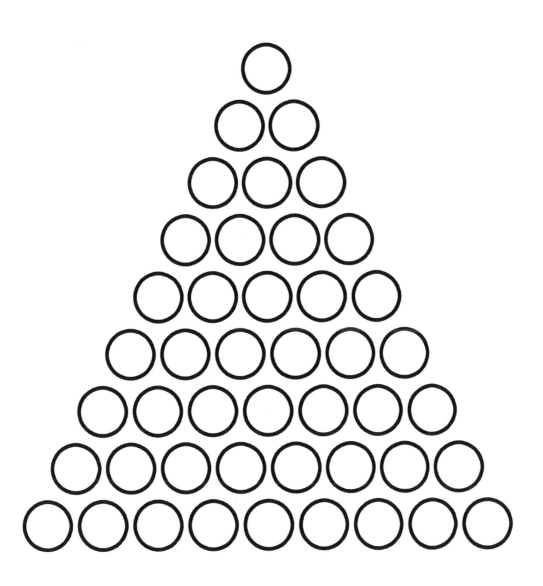

CARDS AND COUNTERS

Color the counters red and write the numbers below.

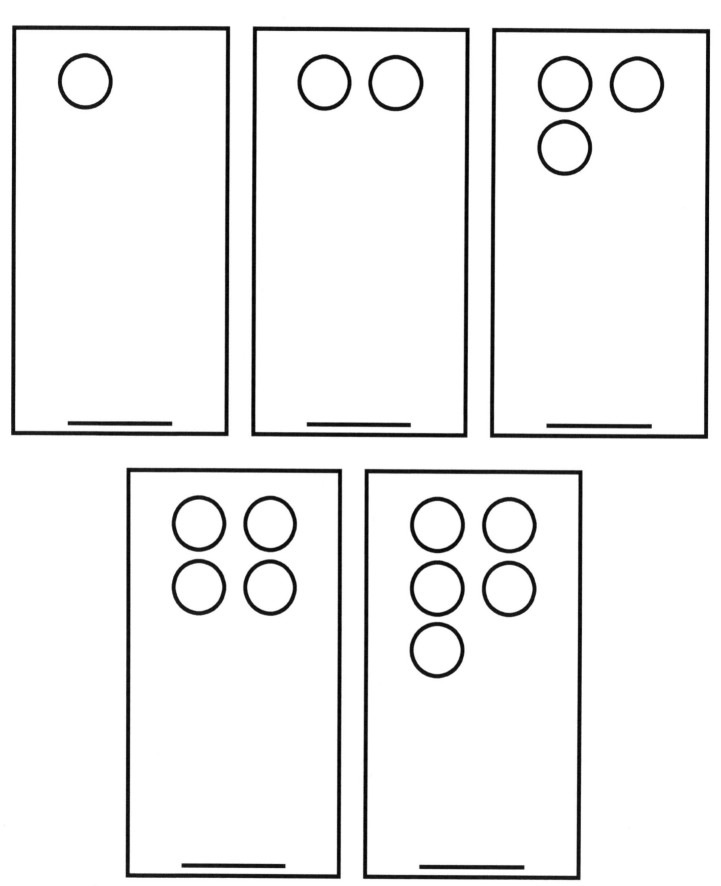

CARDS AND COUNTERS

Color the counters red and write the numbers below.

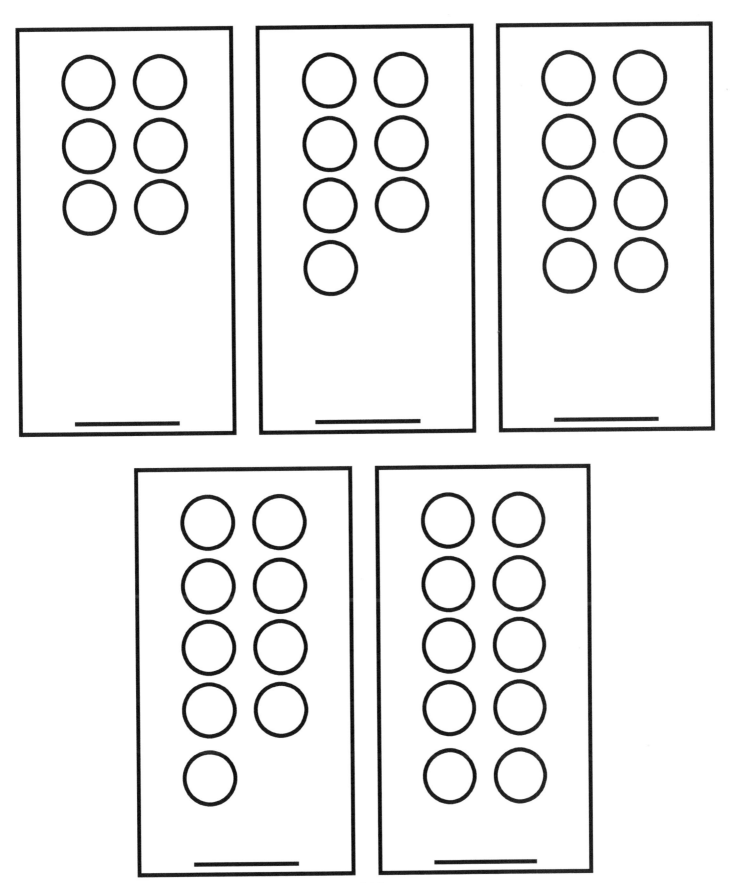

PRINT PRACTICE

1

2

3

4

5

PRINT PRACTICE

6

7

8

9

10

Color 1 bird in the picture and 5 clouds.

How many children can you see in the water? Write the number in the box.

In the pastry shop, Anne chooses 2 cupcakes and Jack chooses 4 croissants.
Color them in and draw your favorite pastry.

Connect the dots from 1 to 5.

Connect the dots from 1 to 10.

How many apples are there in the basket? Write the number in the box.

How many kittens are sleeping in the bed? Write the number in the box.

Fine Motor Skills

Fine motor skills involve eye-hand coordination and control of the small muscles of the body that enable such functions as writing, cutting, grasping small objects, and fastening clothing. Dr. Maria Montessori saw such exercises as part of preparation for practical life such as getting dressed, as well as for academic activities such as writing.

The following cutting strips will help strengthen the child's pincer grip, in preparation for holding the pencil and writing.

FINE MOTOR SKILLS
Cut along the dotted lines.

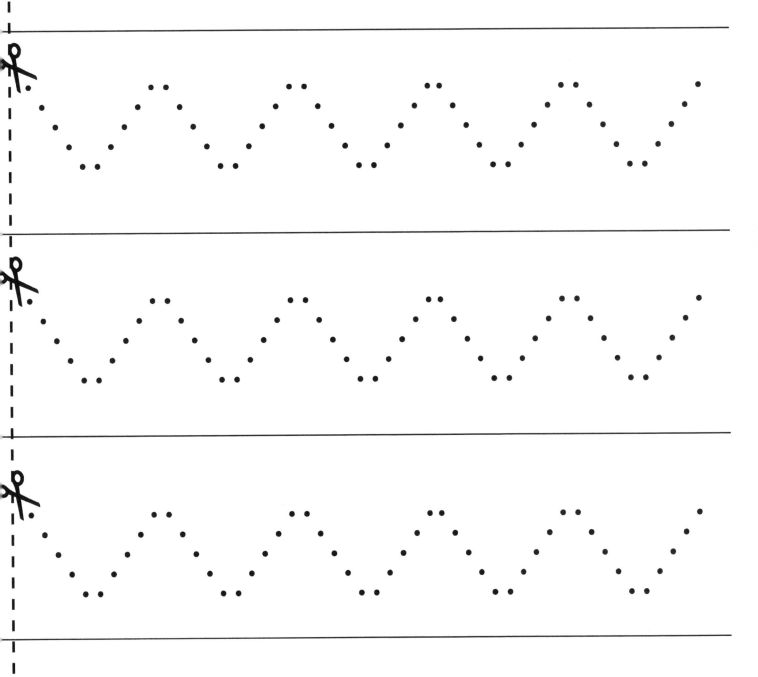

FINE MOTOR SKILLS

Cut along the dotted lines.

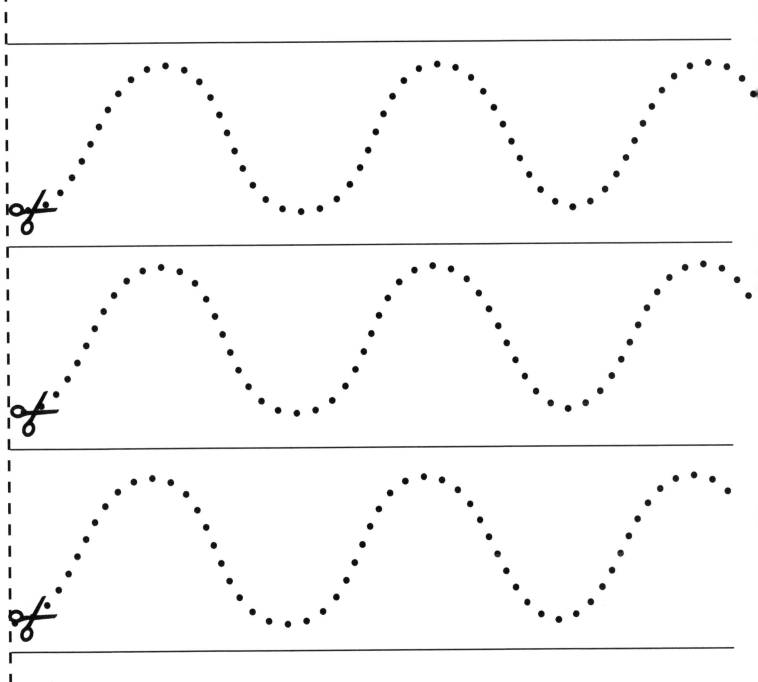

FINE MOTOR SKILLS
Cut along the dotted lines.

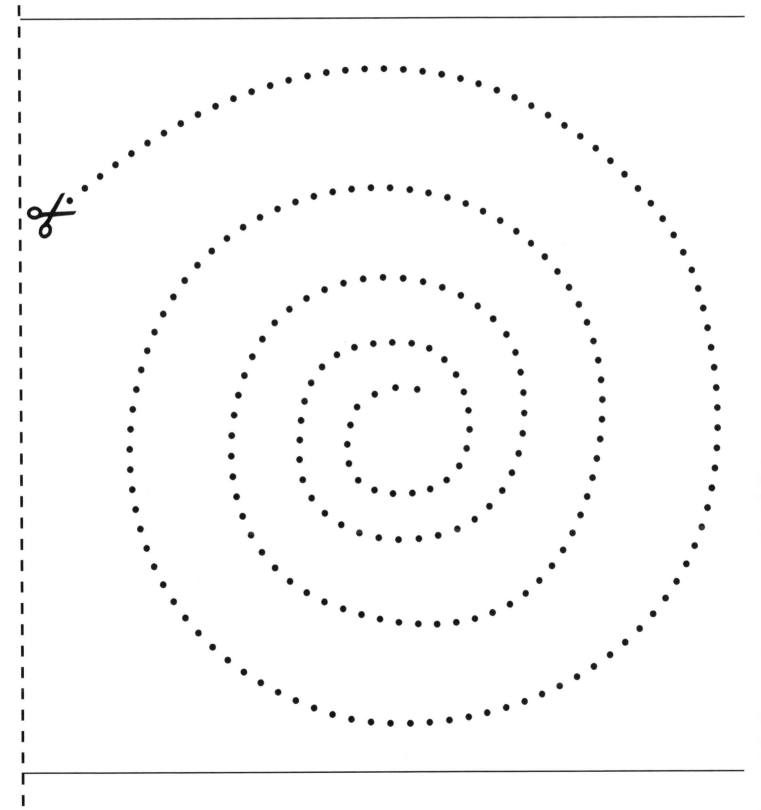

130

FINE MOTOR SKILLS

Cut along the dotted lines.

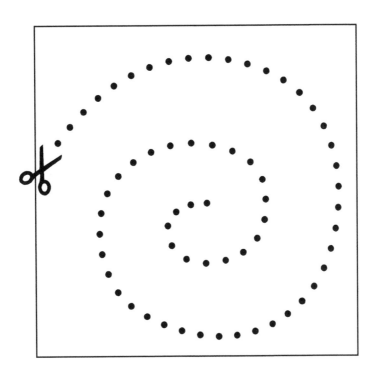

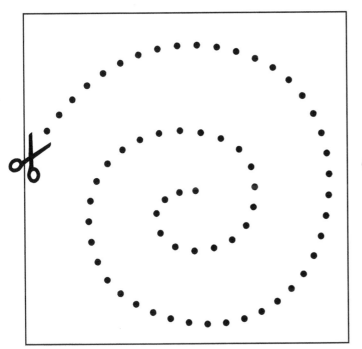

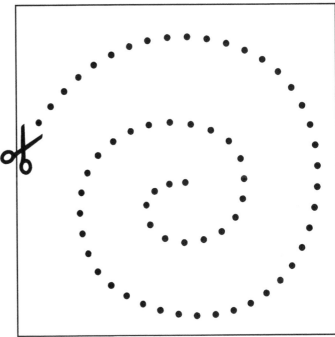

Continue the series of strokes and shapes with colored pencils.

Nature
and
Geography

While children are actively involved in their own development and learning, they are also deeply influenced by the people around them and the culture in which they grow up. Montessori believed strongly that we must consciously educate the child towards an understanding and appreciation of the environment that will in turn arouse his/her sense of responsibility towards it.

To awaken the child's appreciation and knowledge of the natural environment, we need to create plenty of opportunities for first-hand exploration. The child is a natural explorer with a keen eye for detail, driven by an urge to make sense of the world. The exercises in this book do not replace first-hand experiences. They are meant to supplement it.

MAP OF THE WORLD.

Color Europe **red**
North America **orange**
South America **pink**
Color Africa **green**

Asia **yellow**
Antarctica **white**
Oceania **brown**

North
America

South America

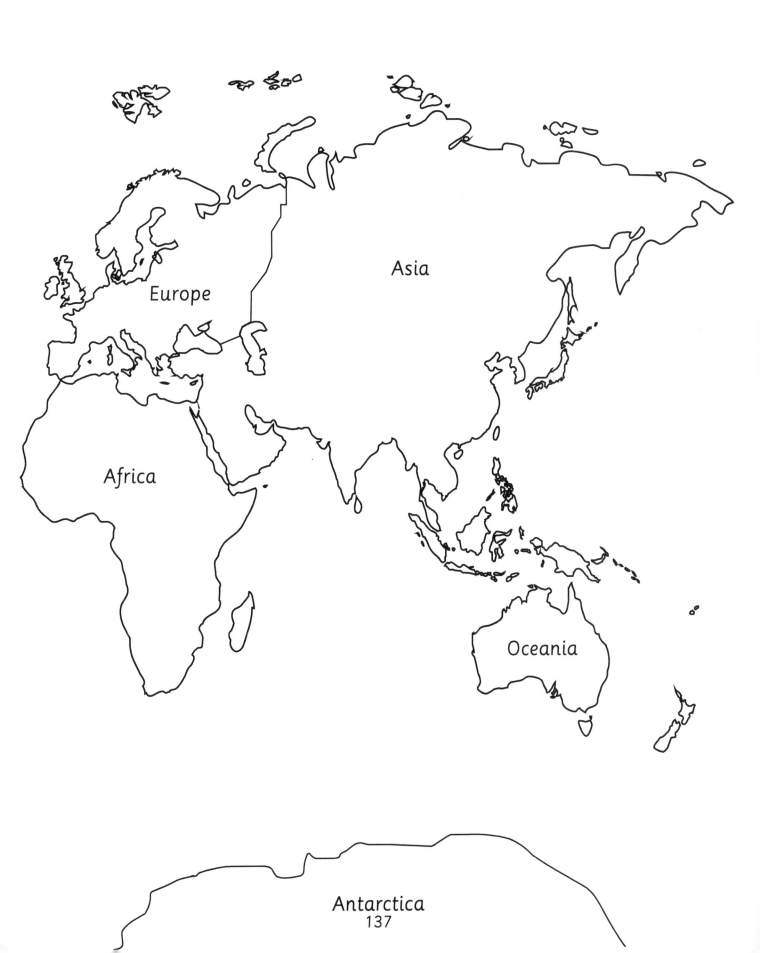

Europe

Asia

Africa

Oceania

Antarctica
137

NORTH AMERICA

Color North America **orange**

Brown Bear

Statue of Liberty

SOUTH AMERICA

Color South America **pink**

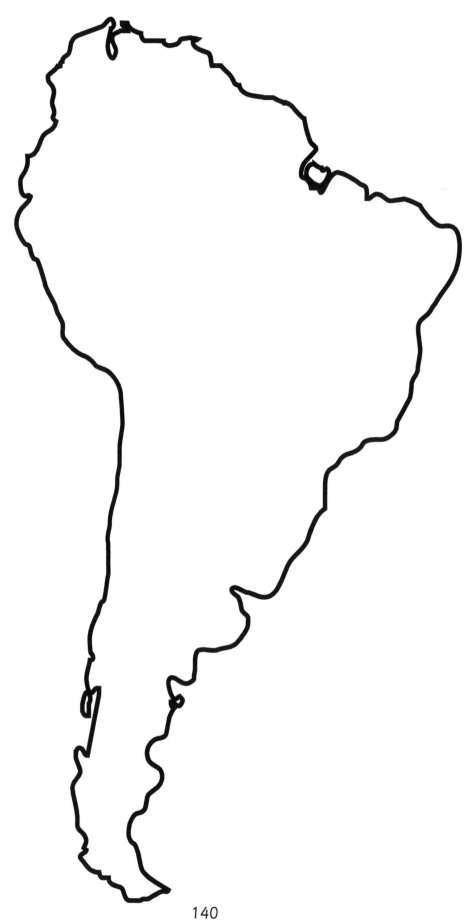

Anteater

Machu Picchu

EUROPE

Color Europe **red**

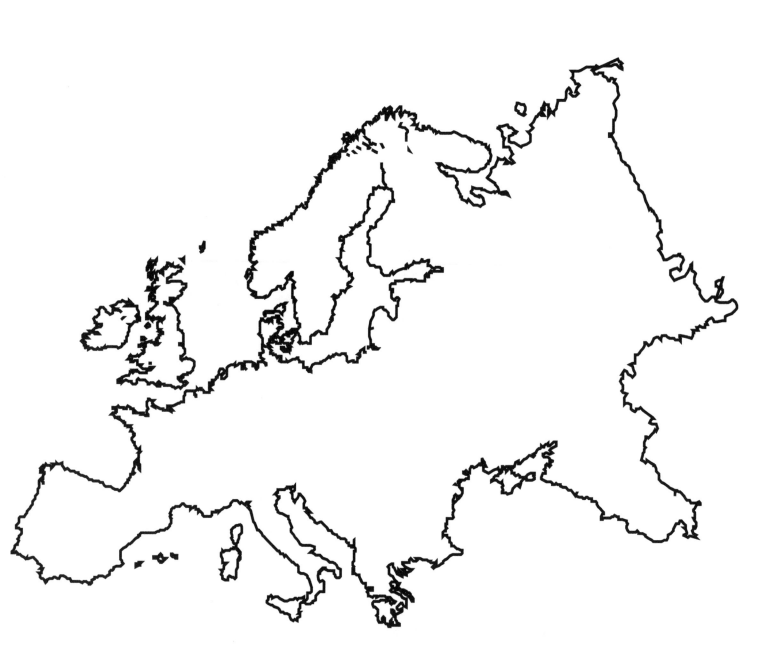

Fox

Coliseum (Rome)

ASIA

Color Asia **yellow**

Elephant

Taj Mahal

AFRICA

Color Africa **green**

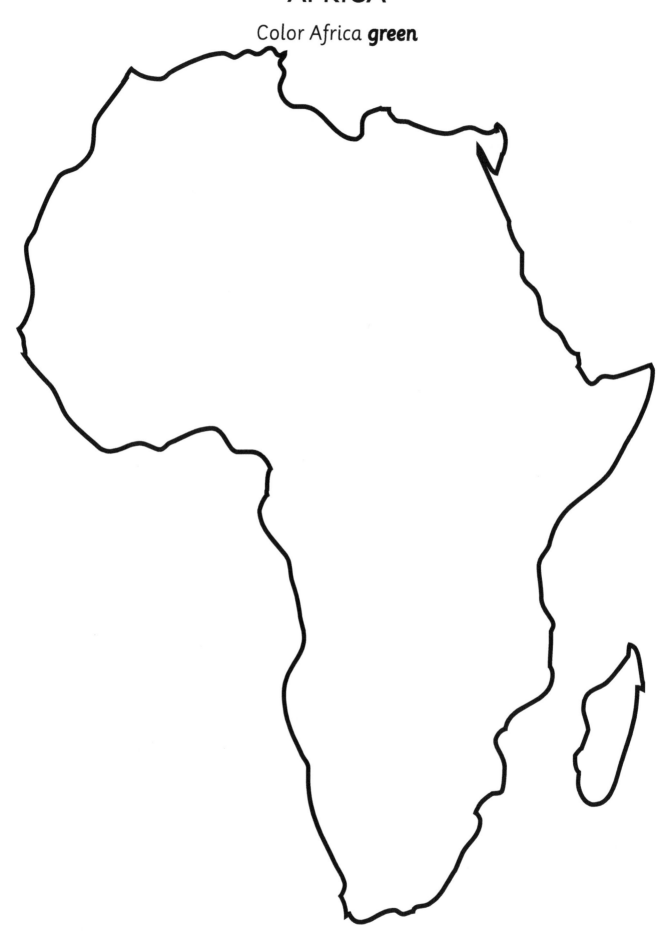

Lion

Pyramids of Egypt

OCEANIA

Color Oceania **brown**

Kangaroo

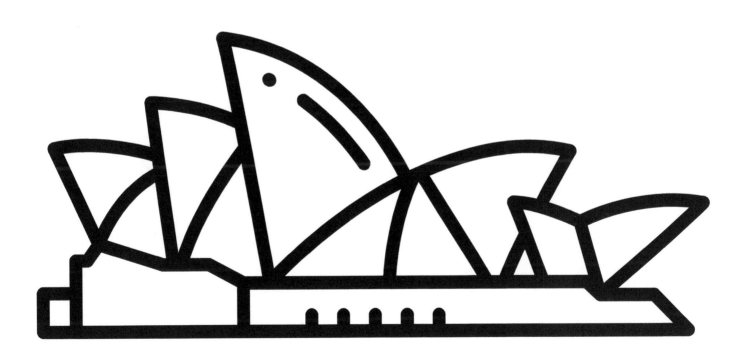

Sydney Opera House

ANTARTICA

Color Antarctica **white**

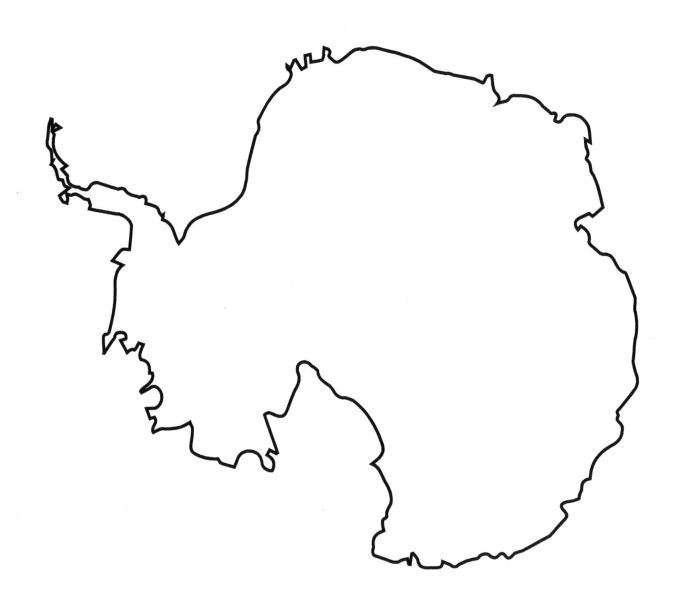

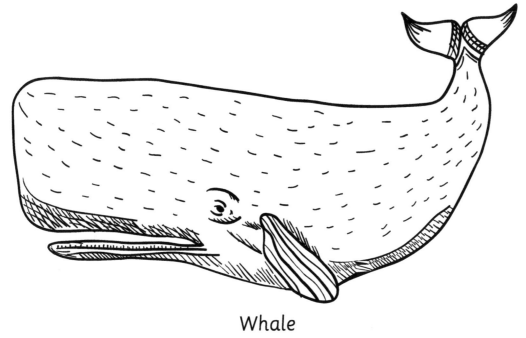

Whale

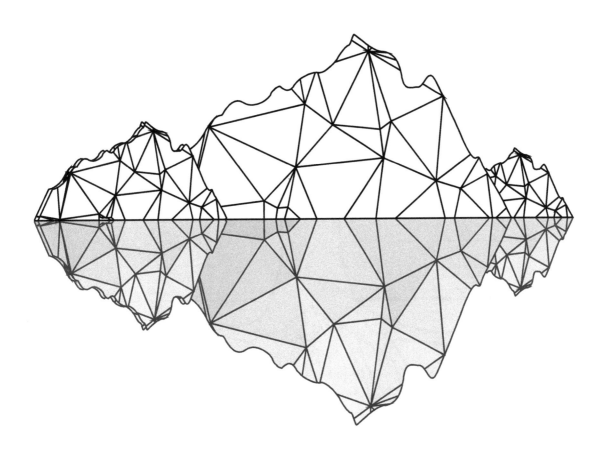

Glacier

Color the parts of a tree.

tree

Color the parts of a tree.

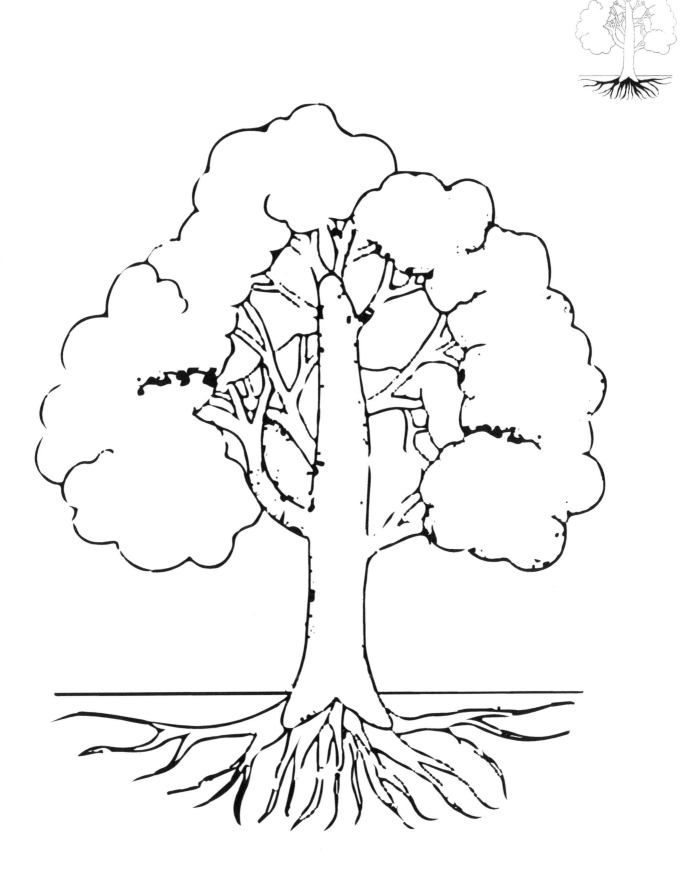

roots

Color the parts of a tree.

leaves

Color the parts of a tree.

branches

Color the parts of a tree.

trunk

Color the parts of a flower.

flower

Color the parts of a flower.

calyx

Color the parts of a flower.

petals

Color the parts of a flower.

stamen

Color the parts of a flower.

pistol

Color the parts of a fish.

fish

Color the parts of a fish.

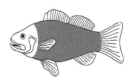

body

Color the parts of a fish.

dorsal fin

Color the parts of a fish.

head

Color the parts of a fish.

fins

Color the parts of a fish.

gills

Color the parts of a fish.

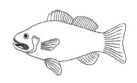

mouth

Color the parts of a fish.

tail fin

"

Dr. Punum Bhatia has inspired parents and children in an independent way! A Montessori Workbook is a revolutionary and evolutionary approach which engages parents as "teachers" in the home and the children are delighted to experience and enjoy sharing what they have learned with their very own " A Montessori Workbook".

"

Marta Urioste, PhD. Montessori Public School Principal.